First Experiences

Peter wants a Puppy

Written by **Lynne Gibbs**

Illustrated by **Michael Peterkin**

BRIMAX

This is Peter. He is very excited because his parents are taking him to choose a new puppy!

"Are we going to a pet shop?" asks Peter, as they drive along in the car. "No, we are going to a home for stray and unwanted dogs," says Peter's father.

"Dogs are taken care of here until they are found new homes," says Peter's mother, as they go through the doors of a large building.

Before they can visit the dogs, Peter and his parents wait to be interviewed. "The home needs to make sure that we are suitable to own a dog," explains Peter's father.

"What kind of dog would you like, Peter?" asks the lady who helps to look after the dogs.
"A little white puppy with black spots—just like that one!" says Peter.

Peter and his parents visit the kennels where sick dogs are looked after until they are better. "These dogs need special care and attention," says Peter's mother.

On their way back to the main building, Peter passes some dogs being taken for a walk. "Dogs need lots of exercise, don't they?" he asks.

"They need healthy, well-balanced diets as well," says Peter's father, as they pass a lady who is busy measuring dog food into bowls.

When all the dogs have been fed, Peter goes to
see them. There are big dogs, small dogs, noisy
dogs – and quiet dogs.

"Look at this one – isn't he cute!" says Peter, as a little black and white Terrier jumps up to see him. A sign next to the dog's cage says his name is Tyson. "Can we have him? Please say we can!" Peter asks.

Tyson
needs company

Peter feels sad when his father explains that Tyson needs to live with other dogs. "He wouldn't be happy on his own." "Don't worry, we will find a dog that's perfect for you, Peter," says his mother.

Further on, Peter jumps when an Alsatian suddenly leaps up at its cage and barks loudly. "He's a beautiful dog, but too big for you," says Peter's father. Peter agrees.

Turning a corner, Peter sees a Spaniel with big, floppy ears. "Can we have this one?" asks Peter, excitedly. But his father points out that Sandy has already found a home.

"I give up!" sighs Peter, sitting on the floor.
"We will never find a dog to take home with us!"
"Don't give up yet," says Peter's mother.
"There are still lots of dogs left to see."

Peter and his parents go up a flight of stairs. "This is where all the puppies live until they find a good home," explains a dog handler. "Wow! Puppies!" says Peter.

Going into a room, Peter sees some puppies
playing together. "They only arrived this morning,
but we've already found homes for them all," says
the dog handler.

"Puppies find new homes very quickly. It's the older dogs that sometimes can't find new owners," explains the dog handler. Peter thinks this is very sad.

"Then we should look for an older dog to take home and love," says Peter. "Come on, let's see if we can find one!"

And they did! Tucked in a corner of one of the cages was a dog with the biggest, saddest eyes Peter had ever seen.

Pippa

"This is Pippa," the dog handler tells Peter.
"She's been at the home for quite a while."
"Hello, Pippa," says Peter, gently stroking the dog.

Before taking Pippa home, she is given a final check-up by one of the vets. "Pippa is fine," says the vet. "She is a very sweet dog, but she'll need lots of exercise."

"You are the best dog in the world!" Peter tells
Pippa when they arrive home. "And you can run
faster than any puppy!"

"I'm glad we went to the Dogs' Home," says Peter. "Welcome to your new family, Pippa!"